BOOK ONE

BELL CITY GROCERY

MY NAME IS T.N.T. JACKSON. THAT'S ALL YOU NEED TO KNOW ABOUT ME, RIGHT? IT'S NOT LIKE MY NICKNAME HIDES WHO I AM.

THEY ARRESTED HIM? I THOUGHT YOU SAID THAT WASN'T GONNA HAPPEN?

WHAT I AM.

YOU'RE HIS DEFENSE ATTORNEY! ACT LIKE IT. I PRACTICALLY HANDED YOU ALL THE EVIDENCE YOU NEEDED TO -

WHAT'S GOTTEN INTO YOU?

SCARED ME!

PISSED OFF.

OH, THAT'S CRAP. NO, I DIDN'T INTERFERE IN THEIR DAMN INVESTIGATION. THEY WERE DRAGGING THEIR - YOU TOLD ME THAT THEY DIDN'T HAVE ENOUGH TO -

WHAT? WHAT SCARED YOU?

EVERYONE LISTENS AND NO GETS HURT, YEAH? HANDS UP! NOW!

LOOK, I NEED TO CALL YOU BACK.

YES, I'M SERIOUS! JUST SEE IF YOU CAN GET BAIL.

HIM!

YOU! HOT PANTS! GRAB A BAG AND GET THE MONEY. NOW!

I THINK HE'S TALKING TO YOU.

YA THINK? JUST CALM DOWN, OKAY? LEPRECHAUN-LOOKIN' MUTHERFU-

THE HELL YOU CALL ME? I SWEAR TO GOD! I'LL SHOOT!

FOR THIS THEY GOT ME OUT OF BED, JACKSON?

MAYBE STICK TO SLEUTHING ON YOUR COMPUTER, YEAH? MIGHT BE SAFER FOR YOU. LET THOSE NOT ON SUSPENSION HANDLE THE CRIME FIGHTING.

MAYBE DON'T GO TO BED AT SIX O'CLOCK AT NIGHT AND TRY DOING SOME ACTUAL POLICE WORK AND I WOULDN'T HAVE TO CLEAN UP MY NEIGHBORHOOD, CHIEF.

IT'S MY DAY OFF. I'M ENTITLED. MAYBE I SHOULD ARREST YOU, TOO. YOU KNOW THE RULES ABOUT USING YOUR -

YOU'RE A JERK!

HE POINTED A GUN AT US AND SHE DIDN'T LIKE IT! WHY'RE YOU BEING MEAN TO HER?

NOW, LET THE MAN DO HIS JOB! THEY'RE JUST TALKING -

SHE EXPLODED ON TO HIM!

POW!

THAT'S WHY WE CALL HER TNT.

YEAH, THAT'S WHY. RIIIIGHT.

AND I'M GONNA TRY THAT ON MY LITTLE BROTHER LATER AND -

OKAY, THAT'S ENOUGH CAFFEINE FOR YOU. SORRY, OFFICER.

YOU KNOW, VIOLENCE ISN'T THE ANSWER. HAS YOUR SUSPENSION TAUGHT YOU NOTHING? MAYBE YOU SHOULD TAKE UP KNITTING. ON SECOND THOUGHT, I DON'T WANT YOU HOLDING ANYTHING SHARP.

NOT SUSPENDED. QUIT. SO JUST SHUT UP. I'VE GOT ENOUGH PROBLEMS. I DON'T NEED YOUR SARCASM. AND FOR THE RECORD? I ONLY USED MY FISTS.

SUSPENDED. I DIDN'T ACCEPT OUR RESIGNATION, REMEMBER, "TNT"?

I KNOW ALL ABOUT ROBERT'S ARREST, CELIA. THE EVIDENCE ALL POINTS TO HIM AND THERE'S NOTHING I CAN DO ABOUT IT. THE MAYOR'LL DOESN'T CARE THAT THE TWO OF YOU SAVED -

I WAS GETTING CLOSE OF FINDING THE HEAD OF THE CAORÁNACH GANG, SANTIAGO. THE CHARGES AGAINST HIM HAVE THEIR %$¢DAMN FINGERPRINTS ALL OVER IT.

LANGUAGE. THERE ARE KIDS NEARBY. DIDN'T THAT ANGER MANAGEMENT CLASS TEACH YOU ABOUT MINDING YOUR MOUTH?

DUNNO. IS THAT STEP EIGHT? I ONLY JUST NOW MASTERED STEP SEVEN.

I'M A $¢%ING DELIGHT, BUT I'M A PAIN IN HIS ASS. IT MAKES OUR FRIENDSHIP WORK.

C'MON. THE BOYS'LL TAKE YOUR PERP TO PROCESSING. LET'S GET A DRINK AND TALK ABOUT THIS THEORY OF YOURS.

'KAY, BUT WE'RE STOPPING BY YOUR PLACE FIRST. YOU NEED REAL PANTS. CUZ, DAMN.

STEP EIGHT IS "TAKE A TIMEOUT." MAYBE A FEW MOMENTS OF PEACE WILL HELP ME HANDLE WHAT'S NEXT WITHOUT THROAT-PUNCHING SOMEONE.

THE LAST THING I NEED RIGHT NOW IS ATTENTION.

I CAN'T BELIEVE SHE'S NOT IN JAIL. SHE'S DANGEROUS.

TAKE A PICTURE, YEAH? IT'LL LAST LONGER.

WITTY. I REALLY SHOULDN'T ANTAGONIZE STRANGERS.

DESPITE HOW I HANDLED THAT ROBBERY INCIDENT, I'M PROUD OF MYSELF.

I STOPPED INNOCENTS FROM GETTING HURT WHILE KEEPING MY POWERS IN CHECK.

$%&#! I DIDN'T SEE A REPORTER AT THE SCENE.

THE NEWSPAPER

TNT EXPLODES!

JACKSON THWARTS ROBB

TNT JACKSON STOPS BANK ROBBERY

REALLY?

SO MUCH FOR KEEPING A LOW PROFILE. THE MAYOR'S GOING TO HAVE A FIELD DAY WITH THIS.

"SHE'S A BRICK! HOUSE! SHE'S MIGHTY MIGHTY, LETTIN' IT ALL HANG OUT."

GREAT. THAT'LL BE CHIEF TANAKA TELLING ME HOW MUCH OF A #$¢%UP I AM.

LOOK, IT'S NOT MY FAULT, SANTIAGO. I DIDN'T $#¢*%'ING SEE ANY PRESS. I BET ONE OF YOUR BOYS LEAKED IT. OR MAYBE –

JUST TELL ME NOW! I DON'T WANNA COME DOWN THERE. 'SIDES, I HAVE TO SEE THAT COURT-APPOINTED –

FINE. I'LL BE RIGHT $#$¢*ING THERE. DAMN.

ARE YOU OKAY, DEAR?

OKAY IS A RELATIVE TERM, DON'T YOU THINK? I'M FINE, BUT THANKS FOR ASKING.

IF THAT'S YOUR FINE, I'D HATE TO SEE YOU HAPPY. YOUR LANGUAGE IS ATROCIOUS. THERE ARE MUCH MORE CONSTRUCTIVE WAYS TO EXPRESS YOURSELF.

WHAT'RE YOU, AN ENGLISH TEACHER?

"SHE'S A BRICK! HOUSE!"

I JINXED IT.

WHAT?! HOW THE $#¢*! CAN THEY DO THAT?

JUST... SIT DOWN AND CALM DOWN. YOU'RE MAKIN' ME NERVOUS.

DID YOU JUST TELL ME TO CALM DOWN? THAT'S SMART. THAT WORK WITH ALL THE HYSTERICAL WOMEN IN YOUR LIFE? OH, YEAH! SHE LEFT! WONDER WHY, SMOOTH-TALKER?

AND I CAN SEE THE PROMISED LAND IN THAT TOP YOU'RE ALMOST WEARING. JUST - PLEASE! SIT DOWN, CELIA. THERE'S MORE AND YOU'RE MAKING ME UNCOMFORTABLE.

I LIKE THE MEN IN MY LIFE TO BE UNCOMFORTABLE.

CELIA. LISTEN.

THEY AMENDED THE CHARGES. ROBERT IS NOW FACING THE DEATH PENALTY. AND... WELL...

HE CONFESSED.

HE DIDN'T DO IT. I'M GOING TO SOLVE THIS, SANTIAGO.

BEE-DOOP!
BEE-DOOP!

CHIEF TANAKA. HOLD ON A SEC.

CELIA! JUST WAIT! CELIA!

CELIA JACKSON.

B#₵%. HOW'S YOUR KNEES? TIRED YET?

BET THAT GAG REFLEX IS.

YOUR CONCERN IS OVERWHELMING, DETECTIVE, OR SHOULD I SAY "FORMER DETECTIVE"—AH... TNT, IS IT? FROM HERE, I'D GO WITH TNA IF I WERE YOU. BUT CODE NAMES ARE SO JUVENILE, AREN'T THEY?

SHE'S SUSPENDED. SHE'LL BE BACK, MS. WASHBURN.

YOU INSUFFERABLE $#!₵!

WHY DON'T YOU STEP INTO MY OFFICE BEFORE I HAVE TO HAVE DETECTIVE JACKSON ARRESTED FOR ASSAULTING AN ASSISTANT DA? CELIA, WE'LL TALK LATER.

DIDN'T I?

WHEN THE VAN STOPPED, I FIGURED IT WAS JUST SOME REDNECK JACKASSES PREPARING TO HURL INSULTS OR CATCALL SIMONE. YOU KNOW THE DRILL.

THEY'RE STOPPING, ROBERT.

JUST GET BEHIND ME, SIMONE. IT'S OKAY.

THAT'S WHEN I RECOGNIZED THEM. THEY WERE THERE, CELIA. SURVIVORS.

AND THEY HAD SOMETHING ELSE IN MIND.

ROBERT!

BACK OFF! DON'T BE A HERO. YOU KNOW WHERE THAT GETS HER, RIGHT, NITRO?

THEY DIDN'T KNOW, CELIA. THEY DIDN'T REALIZE I WOULDN'T ACCESS MY POWERS. NEVER AGAIN.

AS THEY PUT HER IN THE VAN, THEY MENTIONED THE WORD "RANSOM" AND SAID,

"WE'LL SEE YOU SOON."

FEAR IS A STRANGE THING.

STRESS RELEASES HORMONES LIKE CORTISOL AND ADRENALINE.

MS. JACKSON? CAN WE TALK HIM OUT OF DOING THIS TODAY?

I TRIED. DID YOU? YOU'RE HIS %#$DAMN DEFENSE ATTORNEY.

YOUR HEART RACES.

I SUPPOSE YOU COULD PUT A STOP TO THIS RIGHT NOW. HOW DOES IT WORK? A LITTLE RIGHTEOUS RAGE, TOUCH HIS HANDS, OR DO YOU NEED HIM FOR THAT? AND THEN -

THAT SOUNDS AN AWFUL LOT LIKE BLAME, YOU @$$%*%#. WE WERE CLEARED OF ANY -

YOU'RE MISTAKEN, MS. JACKSON. MAY I CALL YOU CELIA?

BLOOD FILLS YOUR LIMBS, MAKING IT EASIER FOR YOU TO RUN...

...OR THROW A PUNCH.

UNLIKE MY COLLEAGUES AT CITY HALL, CELIA, I BELIEVE WHAT YOU AND ROBERT DID WAS HEROIC AND SELFLESS. I'M SORRY THAT THE BACKLASH HAS TAINTED THAT.

YOU MAY HAVE LEFT ME SPEECHLESS, MR. ATTORNEY. NOW DO YOUR DAMN JOB.

ALL RISE. THIS COURT IS NOW IN SESSION. THE HONORABLE PATRICK O'BRIEN, PRESIDING.

YOU MAY BE SEATED.

THIS IS A PRELIMINARY HEARING, MEANT TO DETERMINE NEXT STEPS IN THE PROCESS, BUT... MISTER JACKSON? PLEASE RISE.

I UNDERSTAND THAT YOU HAVE WAIVED READING OF THE CHARGES AND WISH TO PLEAD GUILTY, IS THAT CORRECT, MISTER JACKSON? THROW YOURSELF ON THE MERCY OF THIS COURT?

IT IS, YOUR HONOR.

AM I TO ALSO UNDERSTAND THAT THIS IS AGAINST COUNCIL?

YES, JUDGE. MISTER JACKSON IS ACTING AGAINST HIS OWN INTERESTS AND –

BUT THAT IS HIS RIGHT, MISTER THOMAS, CORRECT? YOU WEREN'T THERE THAT DAY, WERE YOU? DIDN'T WITNESS THE HORROR THIS... DEFENDANT AND HIS MISCREANT SISTER...LEFT IN THEIR WAKE. THE BLOOD. THE SHATTERED LIVES.

I ACCEPT YOUR PLEA, MISTER JACKSON. I'D LIKE TO SKIP STRAIGHT TO SENTENCING.

FEAR IMPACTS BOTH PHYSICAL AND MENTAL HEALTH.

TELL ERIN THAT I LOVE HER. TELL HER I'M SORRY.

TELL HER JUSTICE IS SERVED.

K:BLAM

ROBERT!

IT WEAKENS OUR IMMUNE SYSTEMS.

⟨HUK⟩ I... I TRIED... ⟨HUKT⟩ CELIA... I —

AND, WHILE IT IS AN IMPORTANT EMOTION DESIGNED TO PROTECT US FROM DANGER,

I'M TRYING, SIR. IT'S CHAOS DOWN HERE. SEND EVERYONE, BUT TELL THEM TO KEEP THEIR DISTANCE.

TELL THEM, DAMN IT!

IT ALSO CAUSES PROBLEMS SUCH AS DECREASED FERTILITY, ULCERS...

NO, JACKSON IS... WELL...

SIR...

...SOMETHING MIGHT EXPLODE.

AND DEATH.

Book Two

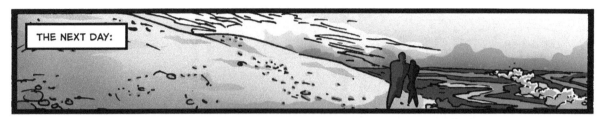

THE NEXT DAY:

"LIEUTENANT! YOU BACK?"

"I'M BACK. SO... WHAT'VE WE GOT?"

"D.B. A MRS. RACHEL NOBEL."

"THE ATTORNEY'S WIFE? THE ONE FROM ROBERT'S -?"

"THE ONE AND THE SAME."

"CAUSE OF DEATH?"

"SEE FOR YOURSELF."

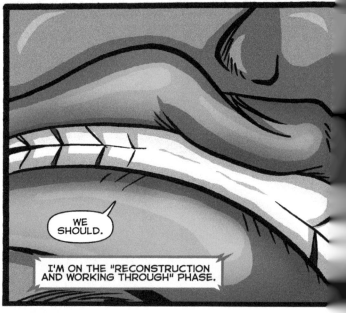

YOU'RE GRIEVING, CELIA, SO I'LL –

AND THEN THERE'S THE CASSETTE TAPE.

TAPE?

A PLEA AGREEMENT WITH AN EAMON BYRNE – A CAORANACH – ABOUT HIS DEALINGS WITH THE BELL CITY P.D.

MRS. NOBEL FOUND IT AMONG HIS PERSONAL EFFECTS. PHONE RECORDS SHOW SHE CALLED YOU THE DAY SHE WAS KILLED.

I CALLED TO OFFER MY CONDOLENCES TO A GRIEVING WIDOW. SHE NEVER MENTIONED ANY TAPE. YOU'RE WRONG, LIEUTENANT.

MMHMM. COURIER DELIVERED THE TAPE THIS MORNING. I SENT A COPY TO THE A.G.'S OFFICE AFTER I MADE A COPY.

WANNA HEAR IT?

GO ON, MR. BYRNE.

SO... CAORÁNACHS? THEY'VE GOT A GUY. HIGH-UP. DEVIOUS BASTARD.

I'LL NEED THAT NAME, MR. BYRNE. DEAL'S OFF OTHERWISE.

GUY'S NAME IS SANTIAGO.

DAMN IT!

JUST WANNA KNOW WHY. AFTER ALL THESE YEARS OF FRIENDSHIP... WHY?

YOU'LL NEVER UNDERSTAND. A MONSTER LIKE YOU CAN'T.

TRY ME.

YOU KNOW WHAT THEY SAY ABOUT KEEPING YOUR FRIENDS CLOSE —

CLIKT

LISTEN TO ME, YOU B*TCH! JUST... LISTEN!

AFTER YOU AND ROBERT... AFTER THE EXPLOSION. YOU MADE ENEMIES. A LOT OF ENEMIES.

THEY'RE AFRAID OF YOU. WHAT YOU CAN DO. BUT THE PEOPLE IN THIS CITY? THEY SEE YOU AS SOME SORT OF HERO. THEY WORSHIP YOU!

SO THE CAORÁNACHS... CITY HALL... THEY WANTED TO PUSH YOU. THEY WANTED TO SHOW BELL CITY WHAT YOU REALLY ARE. A THREAT. A THREAT TO THEIR POWER.

BUT YOU'RE AFRAID TO TAP INTO THOSE POWERS, THOUGH, AREN'T YOU? I SEE THAT NOW. THEY'LL COME FOR YOU! THEY -

OH, JUST SHUT UP. I'M DONE LISTENING TO YOU.

OH, AND YOUR FRIENDS? LET THEM COME.

THE FINAL STAGE IS "ACCEPTANCE AND HOPE."

DADDY?

WHAT IS IT HONEY?

MOMMY... IS SHE?

OF COURSE.

BOTH ARE HARD FOR ME.

SHE'S ALWAYS WATCHING US. SHE'S LOOKING DOWN FROM HEAVEN RIGHT NOW SAYING, "GO TO SLEEP!"

RING RING RING

HOW CAN I ACCEPT WHAT'S HAPPENED? TO ROBERT? TO ALL OF THOSE I WRONGED?

CHIEF SANTIAGO, MY DEAR FRIEND. HOW...

I SEE. DID SHE...? NO.

Michael Frizell — **Writer**

Stacey Raven — **Art**

Benjamin Glibert — **Letters**

Tonny Akbar Mahendro — **Colors**

art by: Yonami
colors by: Alexandre Starling — **Cover**

Darren G. Davis
Publisher

Maggie Jessup
Publicity

Susan Ferris
Entertainment Manager

Lightning Source UK Ltd.
Milton Keynes UK
UKHW050642160223
417096UK00014B/227